GORDON KING

Born in London in 1939, Gordon King, who illustrated this book, spent the war years in Scotland and achieved considerable success as a child in major art competitions. After training at Reading University Art School he spent three years at the Carlton Artists Studio before becoming a freelance illustrator working for a wide range of book and magazine publishers. In 1967 he moved to Buckinghamshire and set up a studio in the village of Chalfont St Peter. He is married and has three children who frequently model for him. Gordon King has staged two one-man exhibitions. His paintings hang in various major art galleries and have been featured on television.

ISBN 0 86163 070 X

Award Publications Limited 1982
Spring House, Spring Place
London NW5, England

Printed in Belgium

Johann Wyss's
SWISS FAMILY ROBINSON

Retold by Jane Carruth

Three R's School

AWARD PUBLICATIONS — LONDON

Shipwrecked!

THE STORM HAD raged for six days and, far from dying down, now seemed to increase in fury. We had been driven off our course to the south-west, and it was impossible to tell where we were. On top of everything our ship had lost her masts, and was leaking from end to end.

"Children," I said to my four sons, who were clinging weeping to their mother, "we are in God's hands. Take courage!"

Suddenly, we heard, above the roar of the waves, the cry of the look-out man: "Land! Land ahoy!" And, at that same moment, the ship received a shock so horrendous that it sent us reeling from side to side. A dull, hoarse, creaking noise, followed by the sound of water rushing into the ship, convinced me that we had struck against a rock.

I left my family in the cabin and went up on deck. Imagine my consternation when I saw the boats rocking among the waves, overcrowded with people. As one of the sailors cut the last mooring rope I knew we had been forgotten!

For the rest of that day and all through the night the storm continued to beat in a rage upon the vessel, and I was afraid that any moment she might break up. The boys slept whilst my wife and I kept a constant watch. Then, at daybreak, I left her and went up on deck. The wind had fallen, the sea was calm, and a lovely sunrise flashed its rose-tinted rays across a clear sky.

Immediately, I called my wife and boys. "Land is not far off," I told them. "We must find a way to reach it. But first let us explore the ship."

Everyone hurried away in various directions. I searched out the place where the provisions were stored, while Fritz, my eldest son, visited the armoury and magazine. There he found guns, pistols, powder, balls and small shot. Ernest ransacked the carpenter's shop, and returned on deck laden with tools and nails. Little Francis, my youngest, aged six and not to be outdone, trotted about the vessel till he found a box full of fishhooks, which he showed us with much pride. As for Jack, my ten-year-old, he re-appeared with two huge dogs, a Great Dane and an English mastiff, which we christened Fan and Turk.

My wife came to tell me that she had found a cow, a donkey, two she-goats, and a sow, and had given them food and water.

Next we had to think of a way to reach the shore, and it was Jack who came up with the solution. "Why shouldn't we swim ashore in tubs!" he exclaimed.

"The very thing!" I cried.

Followed by the children, I went down into the hold, which was now filled with water, and where several large, empty casks were bobbing about. They were strong wooden casks, hooped with iron, and it seemed to me that they were just right for our purpose. With Fritz lending a hand, I set to work to saw four of them in half, so that we had eight small tubs.

We put them together, side by side, and when this was done, I found a long flexible plank, long enough to lay under the tubs and turn up at each end like a keel. Then we nailed our tubs to the plank and to each other. To add the final touch we nailed two other planks along the sides of the tubs and brought them to a point at each end, like the prow and stern of a canoe.

With the help of a screw-jack and some rollers, I was able to slide our tub-raft safely down the lower deck into the sea. She was so much at home in the water that she would have escaped from us in an instant if I had not previously taken the

precaution of securing her to one of the beams of the wreck by a cable.

Before resting from our labours the boys and I made oars, while my wife, acting on my suggestion, disappeared, only to re-appear before us in the jaunty uniform of a midshipman. Very well it suited her, too.

After so much hard work, sleep was not long in overtaking us. By daybreak we were quick to wake and began looking forward to the adventure which lay ahead. We loaded the tubs with as much cargo as we reckoned they would take and when, at last, we were ready, I cut the cable which held our craft to the shipwreck and pushed off.

As we began to pull away from the vessel, the dogs which Jack had found leaped into the sea and swam vigorously after us.

I was afraid the distance to the shore might be too great for their strength, so I showed them how to rest themselves by placing their front paws on the barrels which I had hung out to balance the boat. The dogs appeared to understand at once, and so were able to follow us.

We all rowed together, and the rising tide running inland was in our favour so that we made steady progress. Fritz and I grabbed hold of some of the stray chests, casks, and bales from the wreck that floated past us and we tied them to our tubs. As we got closer to the land, Jack triumphantly drew from his pocket a

small telescope which he had found. I used it to survey the shore, looking for a favourable place to land, and decided to try a creek towards which some of the ship's pigeons were flying. We pulled on our oars with renewed vigour, anxious to be on dry land again.

We landed at a point where there was just enough water to float our craft and where the coast between the rocks was very low.

The dogs had reached land before us and they bounded ahead with loud barks while the ducks and geese, already installed on the banks of the stream, welcomed us with a chorus of quacking. Several flamingoes flew away, frightened at our approach, but we were watched by some penguins who sat immovable on the surrounding rocks.

I selected a suitable spot to pitch our tent, and when this was done, I put our heaviest chests of provisions round the edges to keep out the wind. Fritz meanwhile put some hooks along the edge of one side of the sailcloth in front, to enable us to hook the two sides together and so shut ourselves in during the night.

While the children were gathering moss for our beds, I built up a sort of hearth a little distance from the tent, and soon had a great fire crackling merrily. My wife then put our salvaged cooking pot on my makeshift grate and in it we brewed some soup which we had rescued from the boat. Jack and Ernest had collected some oysters and the shells made ideal soup spoons. Just as we finished our meal the sun began to sink below the horizon, and the fowls and the ducks came clamouring around us for food.

The suddenness with which the darkness succeeded the daylight greatly astonished the children. For my own part, however, it told me that we must be in a region near the equator, or at all events in some part of the tropics.

I took one more look outside the tent to assure myself that all was peaceful around us, and then closing the entrance, retired to rest.

salt. Our grotto was formed in a vein of rock-salt.

When we had finally decided to take up our winter quarters in the cavern, we spent many hours planning how best to fit it out. Its immense size meant that we could have a number of separate apartments, one of which must be the kitchen. And in the weeks that followed, we constructed a large fireplace, with a chimney passing out of the top of the rock in which the cave was situated.

While we were busy fitting out our new winter quarters, we camped at *Undertent*, and our food consisted chiefly of turtles' eggs and flesh of a turtle or two which we caught as they came up on the beach to lay. It occurred to me that it would be useful to keep turtles and I hit upon a plan for capturing some. Whenever we saw a turtle on the beach, Fritz ran out and cut off its retreat to the sea so we could catch it. Immediately we turned it over on its back, and then with a drill we bored a hole in the edge of its shell, through which we passed a long cord. The other end of the cord was tied to a stake, so although the turtle was at liberty to plunge into the sea again or to walk about on land as much as he pleased, he was nonetheless our prisoner, and we could make use of him when we wanted him.

During the months that followed we spent a great proportion of our time working on our new home. We covered the floor of our chamber with a thick bed of clay, over which we placed a layer of small pebbles, laid closely and evenly together.

We covered the walls with plaster which I calculated would be properly dried by the end of the summer. And then I had

the idea of using the hair of our goats and the wool of our sheep to make carpets for the floors of our dining quarters and sitting-rooms. This we did by placing a layer of hair on a piece of sail-cloth which we had previously carded and which I wetted with fish-glue melted in boiling water. I then rolled up the cloth, and we would all beat it with all our might using large sticks. The glueing and beating operation was repeated once more, before we could unroll the sail-cloth. The long strip of felt which we could then remove was dried in the sun, after which it was ideal for our purpose. Our carpets may not have been Turkish ones, but we could not have been

better pleased with them if they had been!

The first of the winter storms came rather sooner than we had expected, and we had scarcely time to make provision for our animals before the rains were upon us once again. But now, snug in our winter quarters, we were able to face the long days of enforced inactivity with greater contentment. And the boys set to work to learn as many different languages as they could from the supply of books from the captain's chest.

For myself, I began to learn the Malay language, as I felt almost certain that one day we may have a visit from some Indians of an adjacent island or mainland.

The end of our donkey

WE WELCOMED the return of the bright sunny days with great joy. But our joy was quite suddenly and unexpectedly turned to horror.

It happened like this. One day, as my wife and I sat quietly talking in front of the grotto, Fritz came up to us, saying, "There is a strange animal of some kind down below, Father. It looks like a huge cable, now unrolling itself on the ground, now rising erect and swaying from side to side."

At these words my wife, in great alarm, retreated into the grotto, and I sent my boys in after her to get our firearms ready. Then I took the telescope and pointed it towards the spot.

A cry of horror escaped from me.

"What is it, Father?" Fritz asked.

"It is an enormous serpent," I replied in a low voice. And he began to look quite terror-stricken, for he knew we could not even begin to confront such a terrible monster.

We retreated inside our grotto, barricaded the door, and stopped up all the openings but one, from which we could see without being seen.

The giant boa, for that was what it was, made straight towards the grotto, and the three younger boys let off their guns through the little opening. At this triple discharge the serpent raised its head as if in surprise, but just as Fritz and I were about to fire in our turn, the monster glided swiftly away towards the marsh, where he disappeared.

For three whole days fear held us prisoners in the grotto. However, the monster gave no sign of its presence and eventu-

ally I decided we must take some action. Our own stores were seriously depleted, and I feared for the animals, for we just didn't have enough food for them too.

After much discussion, we decided to drive the beasts up towards the source of the river in the opposite direction to the marsh, where we assumed the boa still lay concealed.

Fritz volunteered to undertake this dangerous venture, and began to drive some of the beasts out, while we stood at the window with loaded guns. The buffalo and the cow were already yoked together, but Longears, our donkey, suddenly made a dash for open ground, hee-hawing loudly as he rejoiced in his regained freedom.

We tried desperately to call the fugitive back, but he only looked round at us from time to time, as he galloped farther and farther away, making straight for the serpent's lair.

All at once we saw the terrible head rise up from among the reeds, and at the sight of it poor Longears became petrified with fear. He seemed to be transfixed to the earth, for as the serpent approached him, he stood quite still. In an instant he was wrapped in the monster's fatal folds and suffocated in its horrible embrace.

"There is nothing we can do," I told my grief-stricken children. "Already the monster is crushing all the life out of Longears."

Although I could scarcely bring myself to watch the nauseating sight, I was determined to do so, and when I saw the boa had appeased its voracious appetite, I knew my moment for action had come.

As the serpent rolled over completely motionless, full-up after a huge feed, I seized my gun, and ran towards it, followed by Fritz and Jack. I went as close as I dared and the boa watched our approach. But as it was literally unable to move, Fritz and I had no difficulty in sending the contents of a couple of barrels well loaded with bullets, crashing into its skull. Its tail beat the ground feebly once or twice – and then it was dead.

When we had satisfied ourselves that the marsh held no other such monster, we undertook several expeditions, during which we made many new and fascinating

discoveries. Among our "finds" were some light green apples which had a very agreeable smell, and which I eventually identified as coming from the cinnamon tree of the Antilles.

On another occasion, after walking for some hours, we arrived at the outskirts of a small wood, where we pitched our tent for the night. Early the next morning, my three eldest sons and I set off, escorted by Turk, who some time previously had become the proud father of two fine pups. Fan was left behind but, at the last moment, her two offspring joined us.

As we plodded steadily onward the country grew more barren and arid, and the grass scarcer. The only plants we saw were dry, thorny, and without beauty, and we were thankful that we had filled our gourds at the stream. When at last we sat down under the shade of rock for a much needed rest, we decided it was time to think about retracing our steps.

I have omitted to mention that Fritz had on one of our expeditions captured a young eagle. He had devoted a considerable time to training it as a hunter, and the bird by this time seemed quite attached to him. Fritz had pleaded to take his eagle along on this occasion and I had consented. It was fortunate, perhaps, that I had done so for, as we sat at our meal, we were considerably astonished at the approach of some giant birds which I knew were ostriches.

The boys, of course, were greatly excited, and as the five birds, four females and one male, were still some distance away, I decided to lie in wait and surprise them. To this end we hid ourselves in a crevice of the rock, keeping the dogs on leash.

"Boys," I said, "if we intend to catch one of these creatures we must be careful not to startle them, for we could not dream of hunting an animal which could beat a horse at full gallop. Only Fritz's eagle is able to match them in flight."

The ostriches had now approached to within a hundred paces or so of us. Then they caught sight of us and immediately looked disquieted and suspicious. But as we kept in the dogs and remained motionless ourselves, they took courage and came towards us again, examining us with an air of mingled curiosity and astonishment which was very amusing.

They might have come close enough for us to capture them by using the lasso, if our dogs had not at this very moment escaped and thrown themselves upon the ostriches with a great noise of yelping and barking. Like feathers carried away by

the wind, the ostriches fled over the plain, using their wings as sails.

Fritz meanwhile had quickly unbound the eyes of his eagle, and let him loose at the moment the ostriches took flight.

The male, distinguished by his white feathers, was a little in the rear of the rest, and this proved fatal to him. Fritz's eagle swooped down upon him, struck him in the neck, and knocked him down in less time than I can tell. Stopped thus in flight, he was set upon by the dogs and quickly killed.

We were greatly saddened by this, but the incident had a happy sequel. On our homeward journey we came upon a hole in the sand which contained about twenty eggs, as white as ivory and as large as the head of a child.

"It is a splendid find," I said. "But do not disturb them for fear the hen should abandon them when she returns."

I mention this incident particularly because some time later we returned to this self-same spot, and were able to capture one of the parent birds.

You can imagine the surprise of my wife and the alarm she expressed at the sight of our majestic captive, for she feared it would eat us out of house and home!

"It will supply me with a swift steed," Jack declared with great enthusiasm. "I shall call it 'Tornado', and I shall spend all my free time teaching it to obey me."

We all gave a helping hand with Tornado's training, but I am bound to confess that we did not at first succeed very well. The bird was so wild, we had to resort to bandaging her eyes to keep her docile.

In time, however, she began to respond to all the care and affection we lavished on her, and at Jack's command, she would sit down, get up, turn, walk, trot, and gallop.

As we wanted to use her as a riding-horse, it was necessary to make her a bit and bridle, and I was rather at a loss to know the best way to do this. A bit was indispensable to guide her with, but whoever saw a bit adapted to a beak!

Finally I hit on a plan. I had noticed that she was greatly influenced by light and shade, and so I made a little leather hood for her, something like the one which Fritz had made for his eagle. Bringing the cap far enough down the neck to fasten it securely, I cut in it two square flaps like the blinkers of a horse's bridle, and these I attached to reins which could easily be managed by the rider. By shutting one of the blinkers, the ostrich would at once be turned in the direction of the other, where the light came from. By shutting both, she would be directed straight ahead!

My invention worked beyond our expec-

tations, and so superior, indeed, did Tornado prove in speed to any of our other animals that Fritz and his two brothers grew quite jealous of Jack, and wanted the ostrich for themselves. But Jack, I felt, had earned the right to be her master, and I steadfastly refused to take Tornado away from him, though his brothers could ride her whenever Jack was not using her.

A kayak for Fritz

ALTHOUGH WE HAD succeeded in making our grotto – which we had called *Rock House* – as snug and comfortable as possible, we still found the winter days rather long and tedious.

It was Fritz who finally came up with an idea to relieve our boredom as the winter dragged on.

"Now that we have the ostrich as a rapid traveller by land," he said, "we ought to consider making something which will carry us quickly across the seas. What if we were to make a Greenland canoe, or kayak?"

This proposition was greeted by us all with enthusiasm, and we set to work at once so that we could have the body of the canoe finished before the return of the fine weather. First I joined some large whale bones together end to end, to make two keels which fitted into each other. The curved shape of the whale bones and their immense size made them ideal for the job.

I gave them a coat of resin, and then cut three holes underneath. Into these I fitted some small castors so that the craft could be easily manoeuvred on land. Then I fastened the two keels securely together with bamboo, and fixed another piece of whale-bone at each end to form the prow and stern of the kayak. I also bound the keels together with a band of copper.

Using split bamboos and reeds, I shaped the canoe to my liking. The deck extended over the whole surface of the kayak, and I cut a circular opening in it for the oarsman. After sealing the joints with a mixture of tar and moss, the boys helped me to cover the skeleton inside and out with two of our biggest dog-fish skins. We also used dog-fish skins to cover the deck, fastening them down with bamboo.

When at last our kayak was finished, I persuaded my wife to make a kind of life jacket for whoever was rowing the boat to wear. She made it double throughout, so that air could be injected into it through a small tube provided with a stopper. The rower would thus be able to inflate the garment like a balloon and so would float, should he find himself cast into the sea!

We launched our strange craft in the bay one fine afternoon, and Fritz, in order to honour the life-jacket, put it on, inflated it, and walked boldly into the sea, where he floated as securely as if he had been

walking on land. His brothers were highly amused and began to call him Punch.

Fritz made one or two trial runs in the kayak, proving beyond doubt that he was more than capable of handling it. And then, watched by an admiring audience on the shore, he completely capsized it, to the great fright of his mother and the great delight of his three brothers.

Excited and spurred on by applause, Fritz next directed his craft into the current of the river mouth, which before he had time to properly assess it, carried him swiftly out into the open sea.

This imprudent act alarmed me, and I called to Jack and Ernest to board our other sailing boat with me, and we set off in pursuit. As we pushed away from the shore, we assured my anxious wife that we would soon overtake the runaway, and would scold him soundly for his rash act. But by this time he had completely disappeared, and it was only by leaving the bay and going out into the open sea that we could hope to discover his whereabouts. My anxiety was heightened by some enormous clouds in the sky, which threatened a storm ahead.

Our boat glided swiftly away, under the propulsion of our six oars. We skimmed over the waves, and past the rocks where we had first been shipwrecked. As we searched among the shallows for a place where we could rest, we saw a long way off a thin wreath of smoke curling upwards. Then I heard a feeble noise which I recognized as the far-off report of a gun.

"There is Fritz!" I cried, with a joy which I cannot possibly describe. And I fired one of my pistols, which was immediately followed by an answering retort. I felt much happier, as I assured the boys that their brother was not so very far away.

We all rowed with renewed fervour, and before long we came upon the fugitive, calmly seated on a group of rocks, level with the waves. Stretched out in front of him was a sea-cow, or walrus, which he had just killed with his harpoon.

I reproached him for the anxiety he had caused us all, and he apologized, excusing himself by throwing the entire blame on the current which had carried him into the open sea.

I forgave him easily, being only happy that he was safe; and after removing the head and tusks from the walrus, to be hunting ornaments for the kayak, we set out to return to our home base, with Fritz leading the way.

We had not travelled a third of the distance towards land when the storm which I had been expecting, but did not think was quite so near, suddenly burst upon us with indescribable fury.

Unhappily, Fritz was so far ahead of us that, what with the roaring of the winds and the waves, and the terrible torrents of rain, we could give him no signal to come on board our safer craft. Torn with anxiety, I ordered the boys to put on their life-jackets and anchor themselves to our vessel so that they would not be washed overboard by the giant waves. Our sails and

oars were both quite useless, and every moment we feared the boat would break in two. Fortunately, the duration of the storm was brief. Its fury lasted for only a few minutes, and the waves subsided as if by magic. When the sea was calm again,

we redoubled our efforts on the oars, for all our fears were for Fritz in his frail kayak. I was so worried and anguished, for seeing no sign of him anywhere, I was convinced that the sea must have claimed him.

When we reached the bay, we looked anxiously towards the shore, and imagine our surprise when we saw my dear Fritz, with his mother and little Francis. They were kneeling, praying for our safety!

We leapt ashore in the midst of such rapturous shouts of joy that the heavens rang with them. It was a reunion which I shall remember to the end of my days.

There could be no more convincing test of the kayak's sea-worthiness than the storm, so we had no further anxieties when Fritz took her out, which he often did.

On one of his expeditions up-river, he had come upon a banana tree, and the bananas so delighted my wife that she immediately sent him off with instructions to bring back as many bananas and cacao fruit – another discovery – as he possibly could.

Accordingly, he set out on the river in

his kayak, towing behind him a kind of raft, which was very light and strong. He returned in the evening, with it laden almost to sinking point.

Jack, Ernest and Francis ran to help their brother to unload the cargo. Ernest and Francis had already set out with their loads, when Fritz said, "Here, Jack. Wait a moment. I have something special for you." And he handed Jack a large wet sack from which came strange noises.

Jack took the bag behind the bush and opened it. At the sight of its contents he uttered an exclamation of surprise, and performed a delighted war-dance. Then, thanking Fritz for his present, he carried the sack along the bank of the river, and placed it half in the water and half out, in a secret place where he could find it next morning.

We made the journey to *Rock-House* without misadventure, laden though we were. Jack, mounted on his ostrich, went on ahead of us, and took advantage of the

The new beginning

YOU MAY imagine the excitement, mingled with a touch of fear, when one day, some time after Jenny's arrival, Fritz returned to *Rock-house* with the astounding news that he had heard the report of a gun far out to sea.

We searched the horizon carefully on all sides with our telescopes, but could see nothing. Then I told Fritz to charge and fire the cannon, the one which we had taken from the wreck all these years ago. He obeyed, and before long we heard an answering report.

Jenny, usually so calm and business-like, now began to give expression to the wildest hopes. She was certain that the strange ship must belong to her father.

"He must have heard of the shipwreck," she declared, "and set out to look for me."

"Then Fritz and I will set out on a voyage of discovery of our own," I told her.

Acting on my son's suggestion, we disguised ourselves as savages and set sail as soon as we were ready, heading in a south-westerly direction. After rowing for some three hours or more in waters quite unfamiliar to us, we found ourselves under a large over-hanging cliff. We decided to sail around it, hugging the coast so that while we saw everything, we might be seen as little as possible.

Judge our astonishment when, on rounding the rocky point, we saw lying at anchor in the bay behind, a large three-mast sailing ship flying the English flag.

Almost at once we were spotted by two

sentinels on deck who summoned their captain. Evidently taking us for the savages we appeared to be, he began displaying before us some red cloth, axes and beads, as if to tempt us on board. But we decided otherwise and made off speedily. We would make another and more spectacular entrance into the bay presently!

Our next venture into that bay was indeed spectacular. We were on our pinnace, with the British flag floating gaily out to the winds, and the family all on deck! No wonder the crew of the *Unicorn* stared in amazement on seeing our vessel, all sails set.

Once on board Jenny's disappointment on meeting the English captain was understandable. He was not her father, but she cheered up when he was able to give her news of him. Then, to her great delight and ours, we were introduced to some of the passengers, including an English family, named Woolton.

We soon learned that Mr. Woolton's health was giving the greatest anxiety to his wife and two young daughters, and we immediately offered him and his family the hospitality of *Rock-house*.

Our proposition was gratefully accepted, and that same day this charming English family was transferred to our island home, where it was hoped Mr. Woolton would regain some of his strength.

During that night my wife and I sat up long into the night in a very serious discussion. The opportunity to leave the island had at last come our way. Should we take advantage of it?

Miss Jenny, as soon as she had heard that her father was in England, had made it clear that she wished to join him. I was certain that Fritz, who was clearly deeply in love with her, would wish to accompany her. But what of the others? And what of ourselves?

In the morning we had the answer to all our problems. At breakfast Mr. Woolton suddenly grasped my hand and said, "The life which you lead pleases my family immensely. I feel as they do that I could regain something of my former good health if I remained here. We would like to make our home on the island."

Fritz was the only member of my family who did not express his happiness at this news, and I knew what was in his heart. He knew that we would all elect to stay, and he wished to go with Jenny.

And it was Jenny herself who had the courage to ask that we should permit them both to leave.

"You shall both go with my blessing," I said, taking her in my arms.

Some days later, at daybreak, a gun from ship summoned everyone on board. We conducted Jenny and Fritz to the shore where they received our last blessings, and our last farewells. Then they embarked aboard the ship.

Five years have passed since that day they sailed away. Sailors from the ship, on their arrival in Europe, spread the account of our history in every land. And many settlers came to our island until, at this present time, we number more than two thousand inhabitants.

Ernest and Jack are married to the two charming daughters of Mr. Woolton, and have become extremely prosperous. Francis, "little" no longer, and handsome as well as tall, is now captain of a trading vessel.

My dear wife and I are old – at least we are bound to believe this when we consult our mirror. But the freshness of our youth has remained with us. Our sons are still our "boys" and continue, as I have no doubt they always will, to give us their confidences and their love.

What more could we ask?